Sebastian

Flounder

Starring

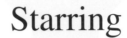

Ariel

King Triton

First published by Parragon in 2009
Parragon
Queen Street House
4 Queen Street
Bath BA1 1HE, UK

ISBN 978-1-4075-3227-1

Printed in China

THE LITTLE MERMAID

Ariel and the Aquamarine

Bath · New York · Singapore · Hong Kong · Cologne · Delhi · Melbourne

It was a glorious summer morning – a perfect day,
thought Ariel, for a walk along the shore. Happily, she set
out, and almost before she knew it, she had walked
farther down the beach than she ever had before.

In fact, Ariel was just about to turn back when her foot struck something hard in the sand.

"Ouch! My toes!" she cried, still not entirely used to the feel of human feet. She looked down, surprised to see something gleaming in the sand. She bent down, dug it out, and pulled off a layer of seaweed. She slowly turned the shiny object over in her hand.

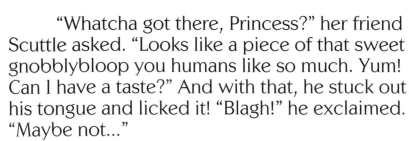

"Whatcha got there, Princess?" her friend Scuttle asked. "Looks like a piece of that sweet gnobblybloop you humans like so much. Yum! Can I have a taste?" And with that, he stuck out his tongue and licked it! "Blagh!" he exclaimed. "Maybe not..."

Ariel laughed. "I think you mean 'candy,'" she told her friend. "And no, I don't think it's that. I think it's a jewel!" she cried.

But where had it come from? Ariel wondered. She'd never seen anything like it in the kingdom before.

Of course, it was wrapped in seaweed and lying on the shore. Perhaps...perhaps it had come from the sea! And if it had come from the sea, she knew just whom to ask about it.

"Scuttle," she said quickly, "please go find Sebastian. Ask him to get my father right away!"

A short while later, Ariel's father, King Triton, emerged from beneath the waves.

"Ariel, my dear," declared the king, "Sebastian said you called."

"Yes, Father," said Ariel. "You see, I found this lovely jewel and –"

King Triton looked astonished. "Where in the sea did you find it?" he asked.

"Actually," said Ariel, "I found it on the shore. Do you know where it came from?"

The king looked at her sadly. "Indeed, my dear, I do."

"Oh, tell me, Father," begged Ariel.

"In fact," said the king. "I can show you. But I'll have to change you back into a mermaid to do it."

And with a blast from his mighty trident, that's exactly what he did!

Gripping the water-coloured jewel, Ariel dived
into the sea after her father. She'd nearly forgotten how
wonderful it felt to swim freely through the water!
By the time she and King Triton reached the gates of
Atlantica, she felt very comfortable. It was as if she'd
never left.

"Why, Father," Ariel cried excitedly, "this jewel
is from Atlantica?"

Ariel's excitement faded, however, when her father led her to his throne room.

"Why, it looks like a tidal wave's been through here!" she said with a gasp. "And Atlantica's treasure – it's gone!"

"Alas," King Triton said sadly, "it's true. Can you believe it? For a thousand years, this chest has kept our kingdom's treasures safe. And then one giant wave comes and washes it all away! That aquamarine is just one of dozens of gems that were lost to us, I'm afraid. And though we've been searching ever since, it's still the only one that's been found."

"Don't worry, Father," said Ariel. "I'll help you find the other jewels! After all, I'm a pretty good treasure hunter, if I do say so myself!" And with a swish of her tail, she was off.

First, Ariel decided to search the old sunken ship – a place she still knew like the back of her fin. In and out of the galleon she swam, until she had found close to a dozen of the missing jewels!

Next, it was off to the coral reef, where it was easy to understand how jewels could be overlooked among all the deep crevasses and bright colours. But with a little help from Flounder and some other dear old friends, yet more lost jewels were found.

In fact, by the time the tide turned, Atlantica's treasure chest was full once more.

"Ariel, on behalf of Atlantica, I thank you," said King Triton.

"I'm just glad all the jewels are back where they belong," she replied.

The king thought for a moment. "Actually," he said thoughtfully, "I'm not sure that they are all where they belong… quite yet." And he reached into the treasure chest and pulled out the first, and by far the most beautiful aquamarine that Ariel had found.

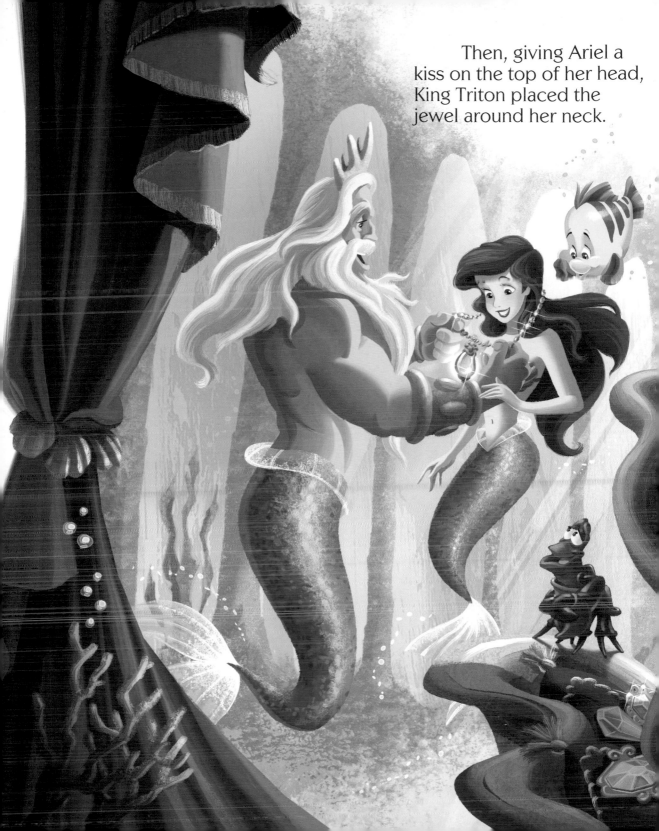

Then, giving Ariel a kiss on the top of her head, King Triton placed the jewel around her neck.

Then it was time, they both knew, for Ariel to swim back to her own castle and become a human princess once again.

"Darling!" exclaimed Eric, when she finally returned to the palace. "It's almost dark. Where have you been?"

And she told Eric about her day – about the lost jewels, the tidal wave and how wonderful it had felt to swim home with her father and to help Atlantica.

That night, Ariel gazed out over the sea as she touched the aquamarine jewel hanging around her neck. She knew that her father and her family were never far away. Even so, it felt good to have a piece of Atlantica with her, always.

The End